THIS IS A BACKWARDS BOOK. YOU NEED TO THINK UPSIDE DOWN AND TИOЯ7 OT ꓘƆAB WHEN DOING THESE ACTIVITIES. SO GET YOUR BRAIN IN GEAR AND START BY WRITING THIS MESSAGE WITH YOUR LEFT HAND IF YOU'RE RIGHT HANDED AND YOUR RIGHT HAND IF YOU'RE LEFT HANDED:

I PROMISE TO THINK BACKWARDS WHEN USING THIS KOOB.

I promise to think
backwards when using
this KOOB

SIGNED: AILUJ

(I HOPE YOU SIGNED YOUR NAME BACKWARDS)

MIRROR
MIRROR
DECODE THESE INSTRUCTIONS
WITH A MIRROR.

1. FIND A CAP AND WEAR IT BACKWARDS.

2. PUT YOUR TOP ON BACK TO FRONT.

3. PULL YOUR TROUSERS ON THE WRONG WAY ROUND.

4. TELL A FAMILY MEMBER THE WAY YOU WERE WHEN YOU CHANGED YOUR MIND. GETTING DRESSED AND YOU'RE STUCK LIKE THIS!

HOLD A PENCIL IN YOUR
TOES
AND DRAW ON THIS PAGE.

WRITE A SECRET MESSAGE AND THEN...

1

2

3

GLUE THESE TWO PAGES TOGETHER.

Write the alphabet backwards with the letters back to front.

CAN YOU READ THIS  TINY WRITING?

WELL DONE, YOU CAN READ THIS! DID YOU USE A MAGNIFYING GLASS? NOW TRY AND WRITE THIS SMALL.

Yo yo yo my name is julia and I'm writing small.
I had to sharpen my pencil really sharp to
get THIS small!!!

This rainbow is upside down and made up of unusual colours. What are they?

What's at the
beginning of the
rainbow?

PUT SOME LIPSTICK ON AND THEN TAKE IT OFF

13

BY FILLING THESE PAGES WITH KISSES.

TEAR THIS PAGE OUT OF THE BOOK. CUT A HOLE IN THE CENTRE. STICK ONE EDGE TO THE SIDE OF AN OPEN DOOR AND TRY TO FLY YOUR PAPER AEROPLANE THROUGH IT.

Cut here!

Colour this page...

...but remember to think backwards, so leave the page blank and colour the edges instead.

Combine two fruits to make
something new. Give each one
a name, then draw them.

banga

Appange!

Give these objects some texture by holding the pages over a tree trunk and then making some rubbings.

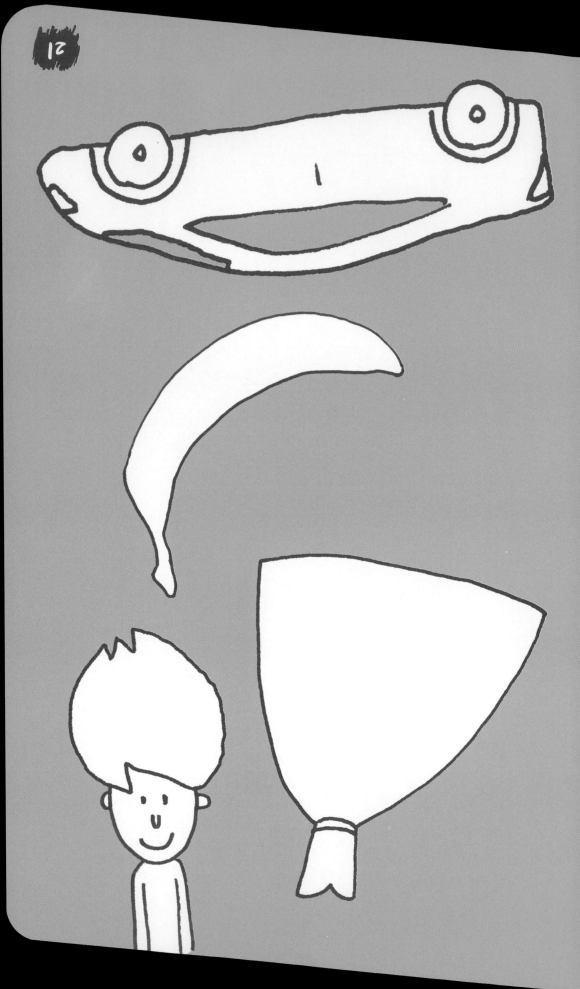

NOW COUNT HOW MANY DOTS YOU DREW.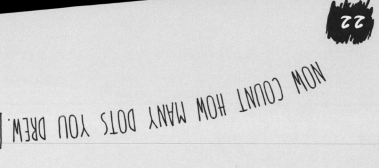

DRAW A LARGE DOT USING SMALL DOTS.

NOW JOIN ALL THE DOTS.

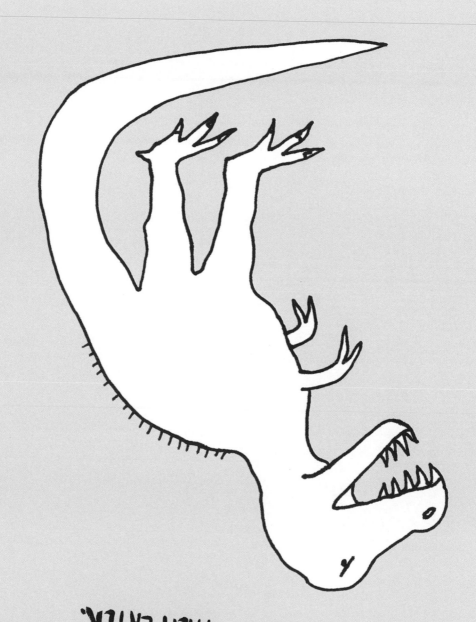

CUT OUT THESE SHAPES AND
FIND OUT WHERE TO USE
THEM LATER.

Stick your T. rex stencil shape on this page
so it looks like he's biting this person's
head off. Colour him in.

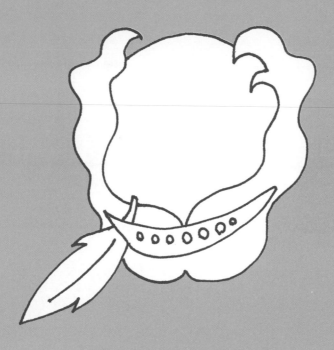

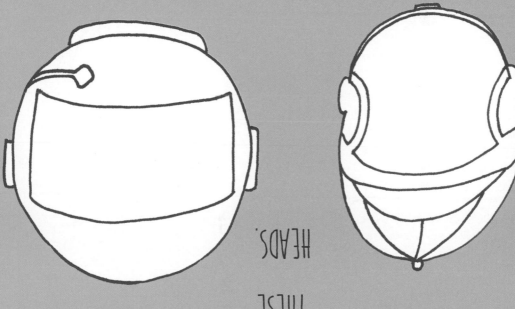

DRAW OR STICK A PHOTO OF YOUR FACE IN THESE HEADS.

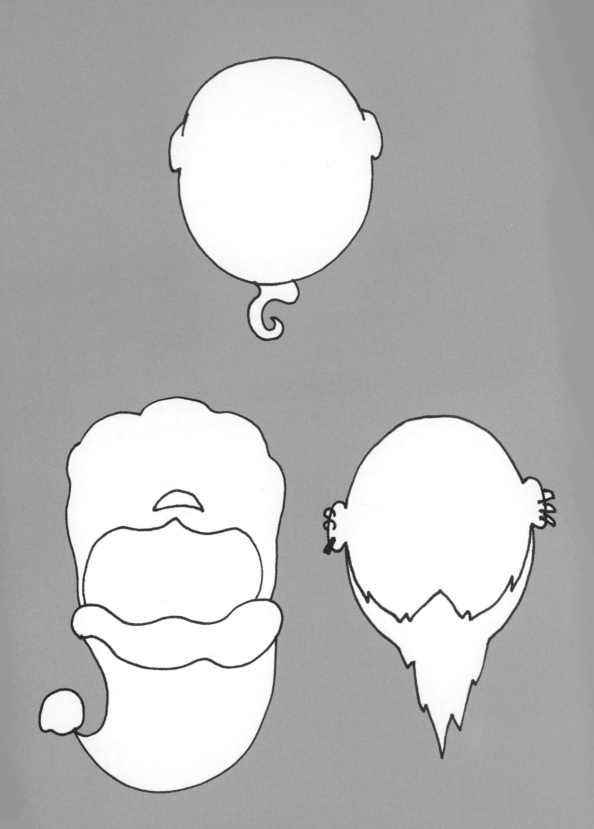

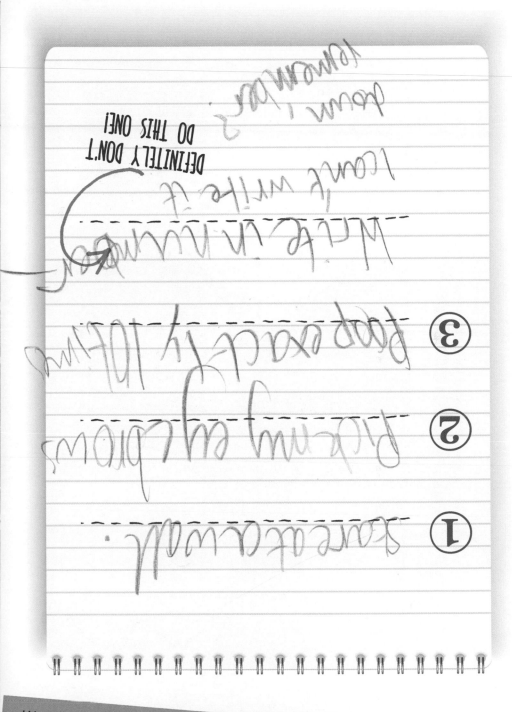

WRITE A LIST OF SEVEN THINGS TO DO THIS WEEK...

1. Stare at a wall.

2. Pick my eyebrows

3. Flap excitedly. 101 times

Write in number

I can't write it

DEFINITELY DON'T
DO THIS ONE!

damn, I
remember?

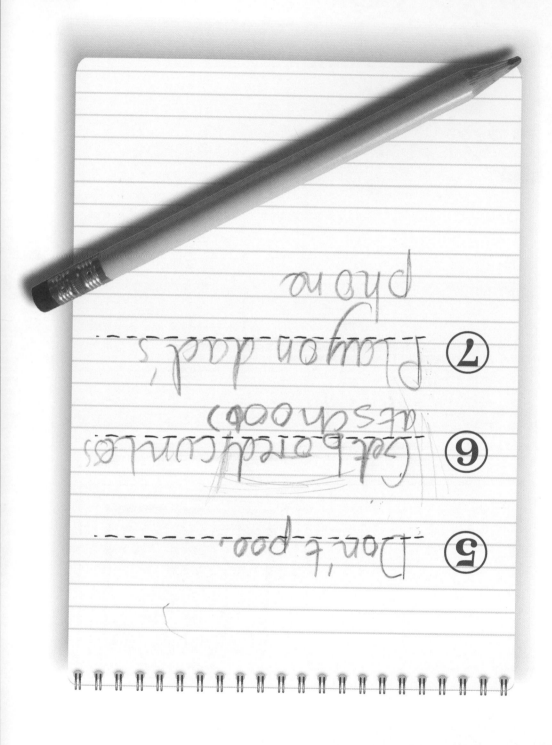

⑤ Don't poo.

⑥ Get oredicurtes (at school?)

⑦ Play on dad's phone

...AND THEN DON'T DO THEM.

TIME HOW LONG IT TAKES YOU TO COPY THIS VASE OF FLOWERS THREE TIMES.

NOW TAPE THREE DIFFERENT PENCILS TOGETHER
AND TIME HOW LONG IT TAKES YOU TO DRAW
THE SAME VASE THREE TIMES.

USE YOUR
STEGOSAURUS
STENCIL SHAPE TO CUT
A HOLE IN THE CENTRE OF PAGE 35.

GLUE SHADED AREA

CREATE DINOSAUR SKIN ON THIS PAGE BY STICKING IN PIECES OF ONION SKIN, ORANGE PEEL OR OLD LEAVES.

THEN TURN BACK THE PREVIOUS PAGE AND STICK IT DOWN OVER THE SKIN TO CREATE YOUR 3D STEGOSAURUS.

GLUE SHADED AREA

There are four giant letters on pages 38-41. Work out what word they spell and write it here:

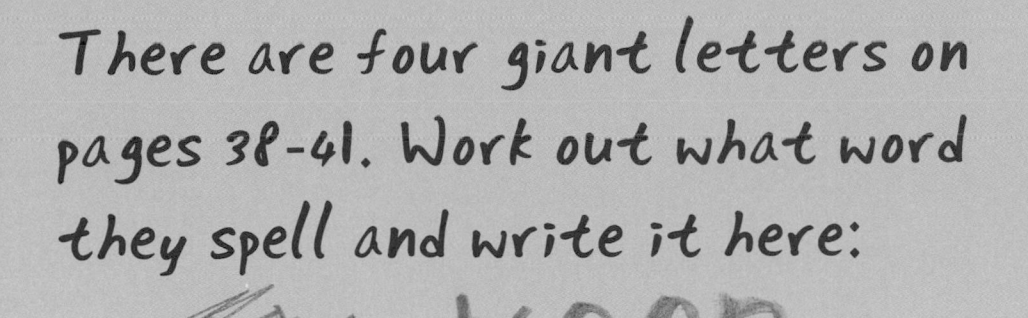

KOOB

Clue: remember to think upside down and back to front.

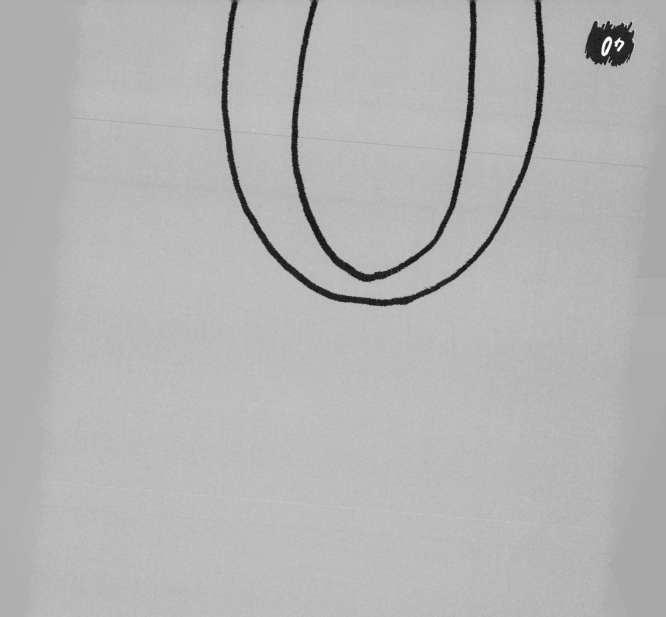

UNBAKE THIS CAKE BY DRAWING THE INGREDIENTS THAT WENT INTO IT.

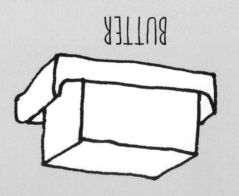

BUTTER

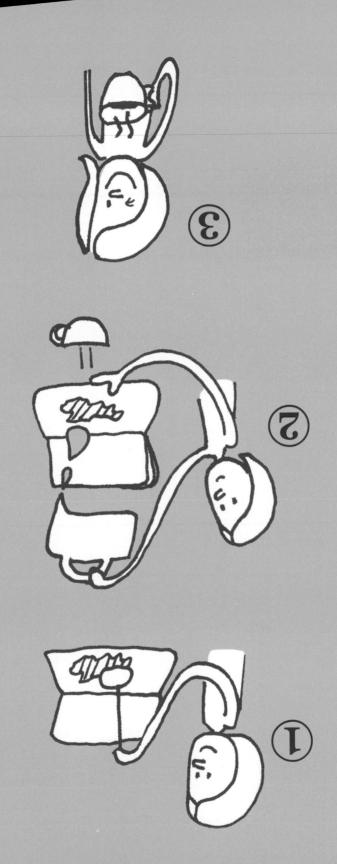

Tear this page out of the koob.
Scrunch it up. Throw it in the bin.

Retrieve this page from the bin. Ask an adult to help you iron it flat. Stick it back into the koob.

47

Little toe

Fourth toe

Middle toe

Second toe

Big toe

Pinky

Index finger

Middle finger

Forefinger

Thumb

MAKE REVERSE FINGERPRINTS BY DIPPING YOUR NAILS IN INK AND PRESSING THEM ONTO THE PAGE. COMPARE THEM TO YOUR TOENAIL PRINTS.

Get a pencil and fill these pages with scribbles! Then use a rubber to draw in the scribbles by rubbing them out.

REDRAW THE COVER OF THIS KOOB AS IF IT WERE A FORWARDS BOOK NOT A BACKWARDS BOOK.

COVER THESE PAGES IN CLEAR TAPE, WRITE ON THEM WITH FELT TIPS, THEN WIPE THEM CLEAN.

Cut out this shape then turn the page.

Stick a picture of you wearing your clothes back to front on page 56. Then tape this picture frame around it.

(1) Place the foob behind you.

(2) Get a mirror and hold it in front of you so you can see the foob.

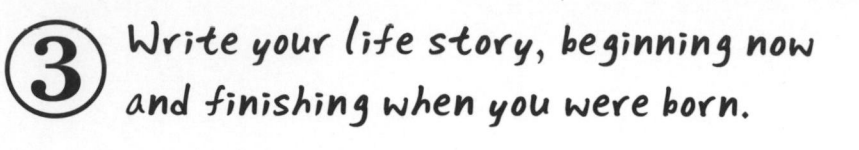

3 Write your life story, beginning now and finishing when you were born.

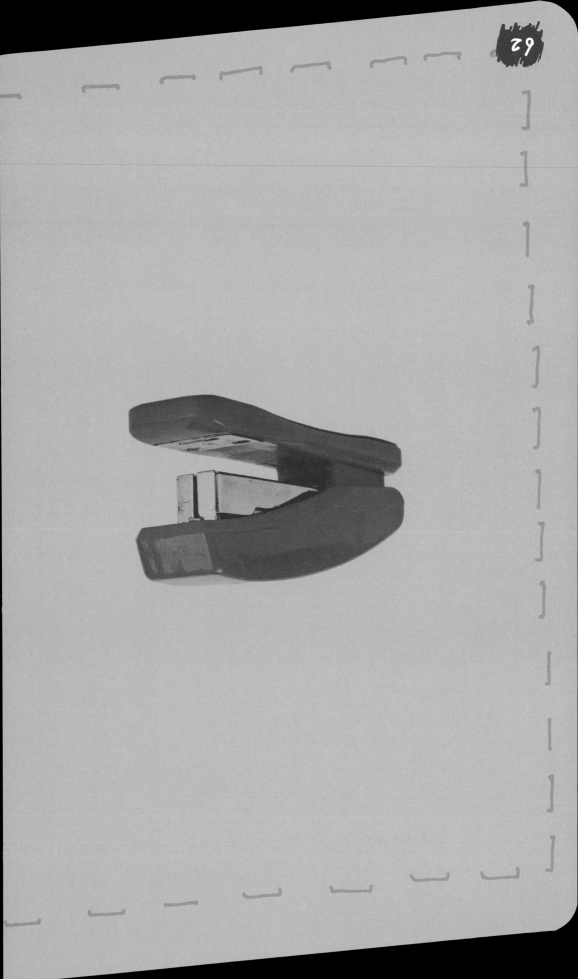

STAPLE THESE TWO PAGES
TOGETHER.

Use a white pencil to draw stars in the sky.

Make some constellations.

WRITE THE NUMBERS 1 TO 50 BACKWARDS...

...WITH THE NUMBERS BACK TO FRONT.

COLOUR THE LINES, NOT THE SPACE INSIDE THEM.

DRAW A SCENE ONTO THIS PAGE
AND THEN CUT OUT THE JIGSAW SHAPES.
STICK THE PIECES BACK INTO THE BOOK
IN THE WRONG POSITION.

73

STICK YOUR MUDDLED JIGSAW PIECES HERE.

WRITE YOUR AND
YOUR FAMILY'S NAMES

!SDRAWKCAB

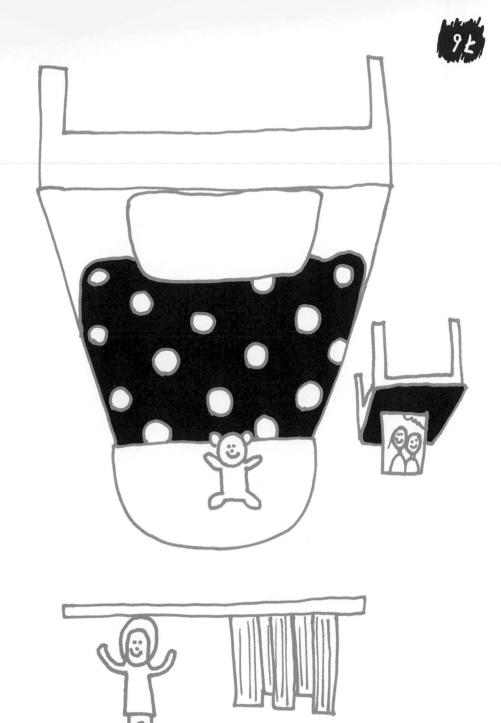

TURN TEN ITEMS IN YOUR BEDROOM BACKWARDS AND GET A FRIEND TO TRY AND SPOT THEM ALL.

USE MASKING TAPE TO CREATE SHAPES ON THIS PAGE. THEN PAINT OVER EVERYTHING
USING AS MANY COLOURS AS YOU WANT. WHEN THE PAINT HAS DRIED, PEEL OFF THE
MASKING TAPE. PRESENT YOUR MASTERPIECE AS A WORK OF MODERN ART.

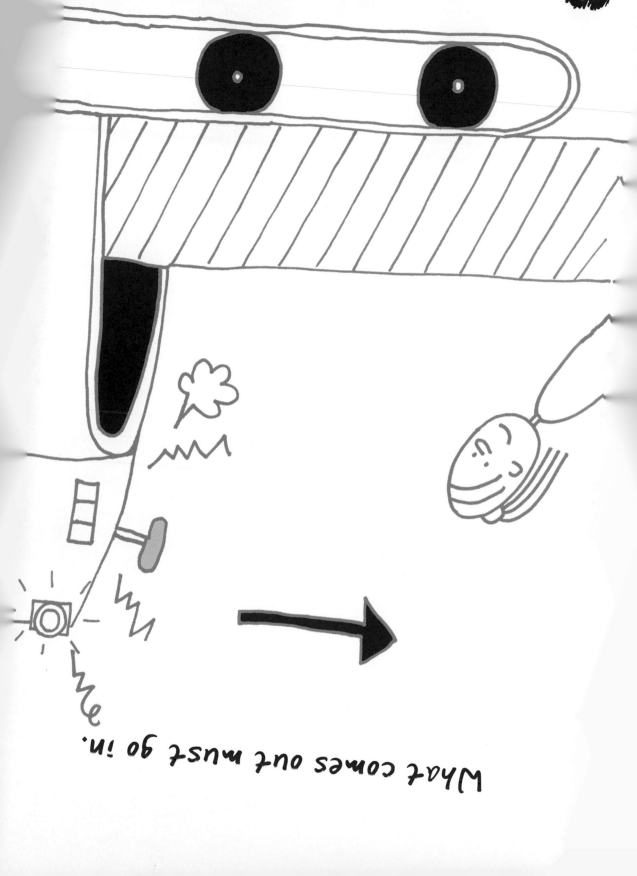

What comes out must go in.

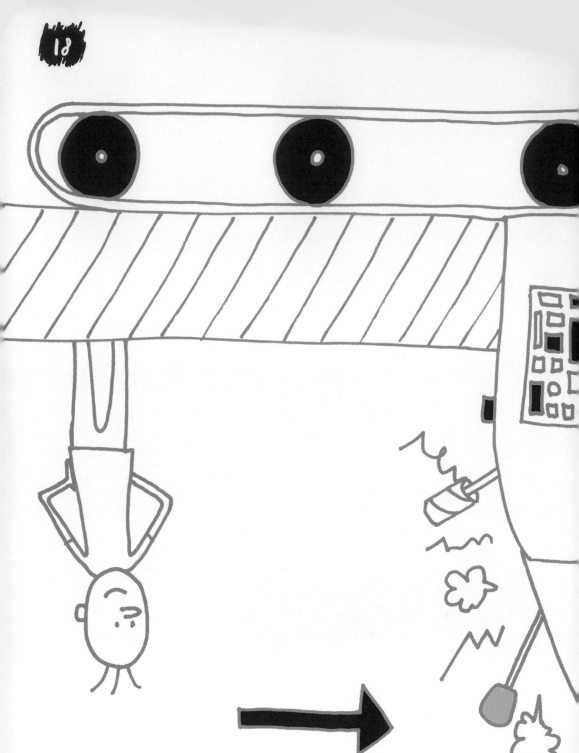

HOW MANY PALINDROMES
CAN YOU WRITE HERE?
(REMEMBER A PALINDROME IS A WORD OR PHRASE THAT READS THE SAME FORWARDS AND BACKWARDS)

LEVEL

Cover these pages in glitter!

Now try and get every single
piece of glitter off the page.

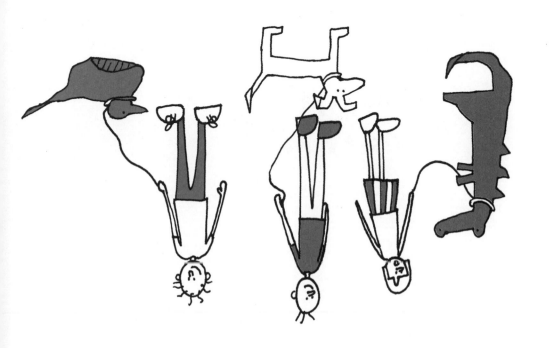

DRAW AN ANIMAL ON THE OPPOSITE PAGE AND
THEN CUT IT OUT. ATTACH A PIECE OF STRING
TO IT AND TAKE IT FOR A WALK.

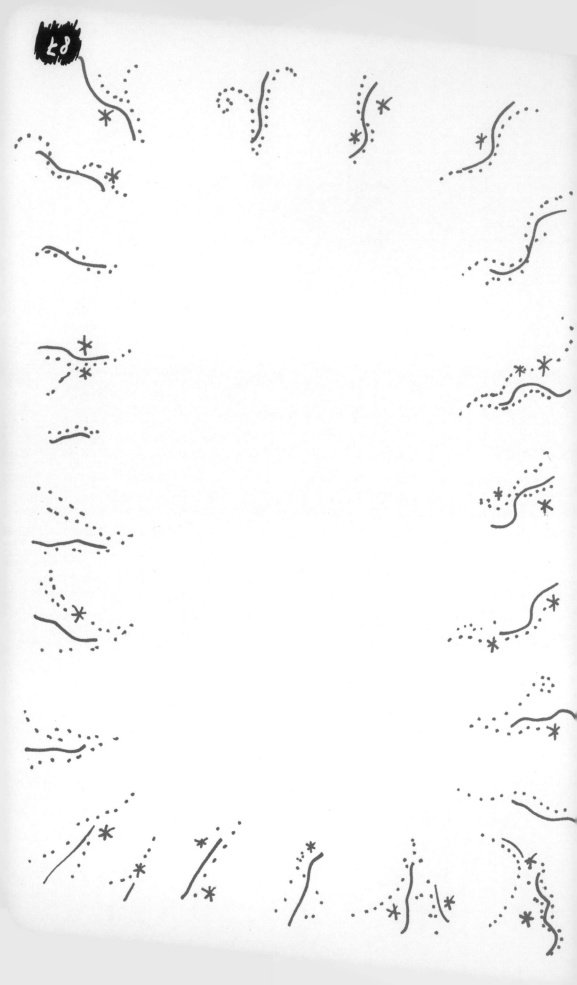

DRAW WITH YOUR FINGERNAIL.

PRESS HARD AND YOU SHOULD MAKE INDENTS ON THE PAGE.

USE A RUBBER TO ERASE THIS DOT. KEEP GOING UNTIL YOU'VE RUBBED A HOLE THROUGH THE PAPER.

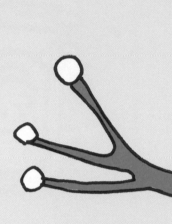
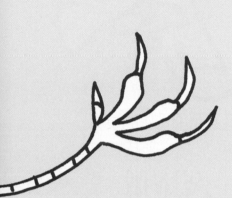

GET AN ANIMAL TO MAKE A
PAW PRINT
ON THIS PAGE.

93

BREAKFAST:
START BY SLURPING MILK OUT OF
YOUR BOWL, THEN EAT DRY CEREAL.

EAT YOUR MEALS
BACKWARDS
TODAY.

DINNER:
EAT YOUR DESSERT FIRST, THEN YOUR MAIN COURSE, THEN ASK FOR A STARTER TO FINISH.

LUNCH:
SIT ON YOUR CHAIR WITH YOUR BACK TO THE TABLE AND EAT FACING THE WRONG WAY.

Tear out this page and
stick it under a table.

Lie on the floor and draw a
MASTERPIECE
on it.

See how long it takes for
someone to discover it's there.

FILL THIS PAGE WITH TRIANGLES.

equilateral

right-angled

obtuse

isosceles

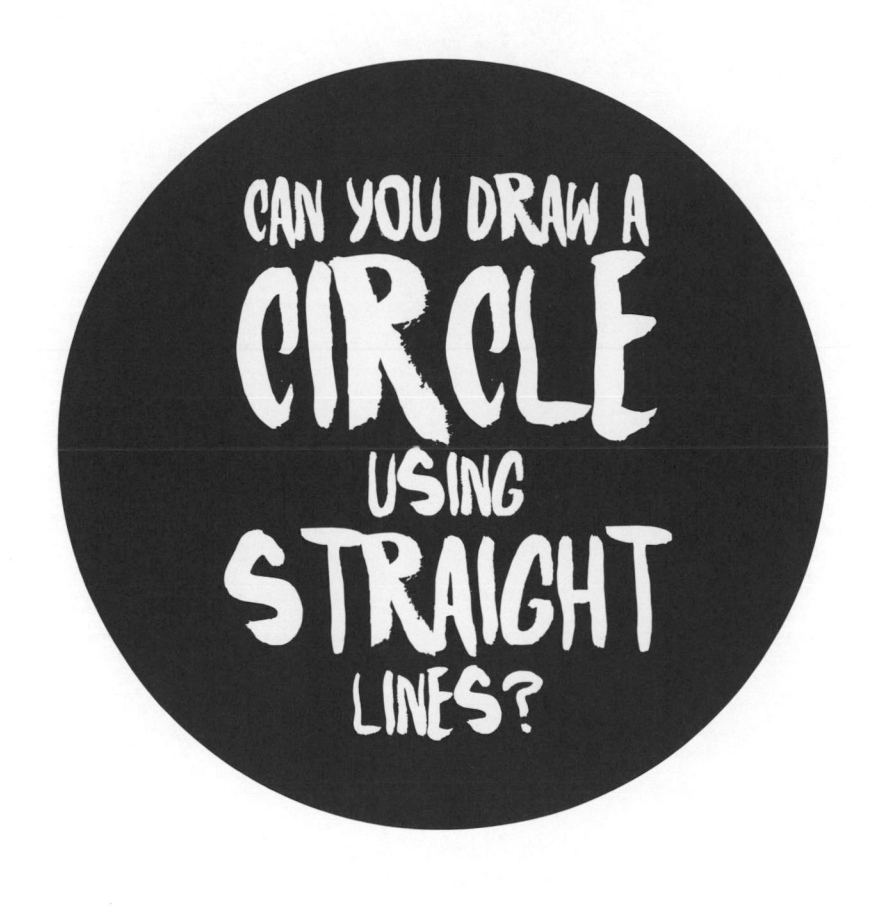

CAN YOU DRAW A **CIRCLE** USING **STRAIGHT** LINES?

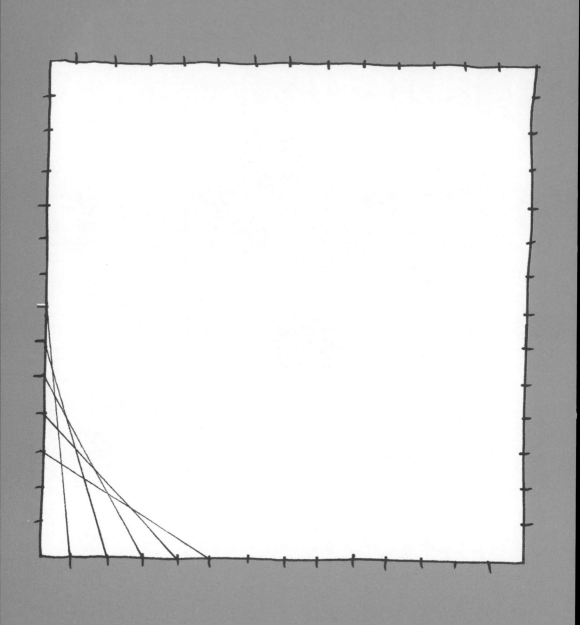

WEAVE THIS PAGE

USING PAPER FROM PAGE 105.

1 CUT ALONG THE DOTTED LINES ON PAGE 103 (NOT ALL THE WAY TO THE EDGES).

2 CUT PAGE 105 OUT OF THE KOOB.

3 CUT PAGE 105 INTO STRIPS, ALONG THE DOTTED LINES.

4 WEAVE THE STRIPS INTO PAGE 103, ONE OVER, ONE UNDER.

5 GLUE DOWN THE ENDS OF THE STRIPS.

BEARD
OR
HAIR?

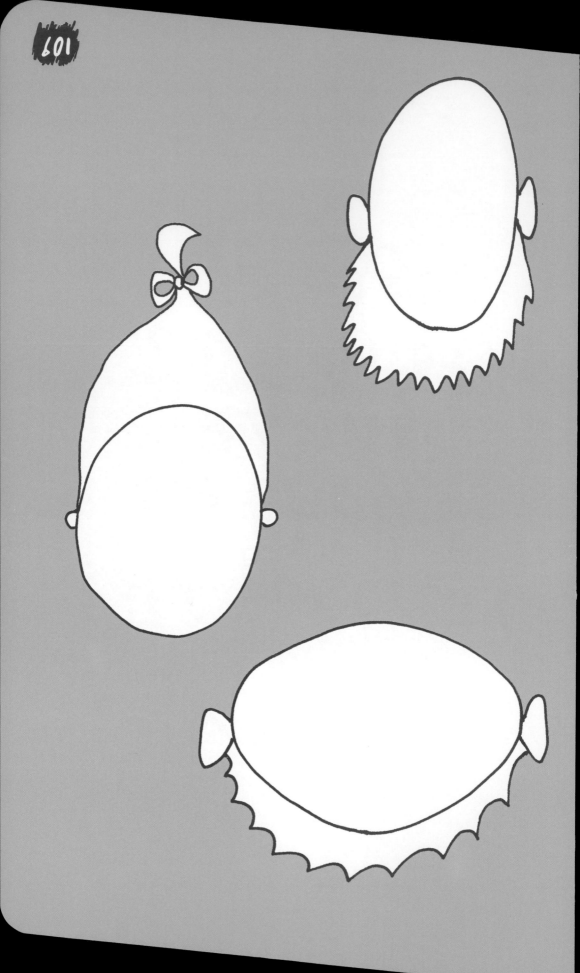

Draw
a
self-portrait
without
taking
your pen off
the page.

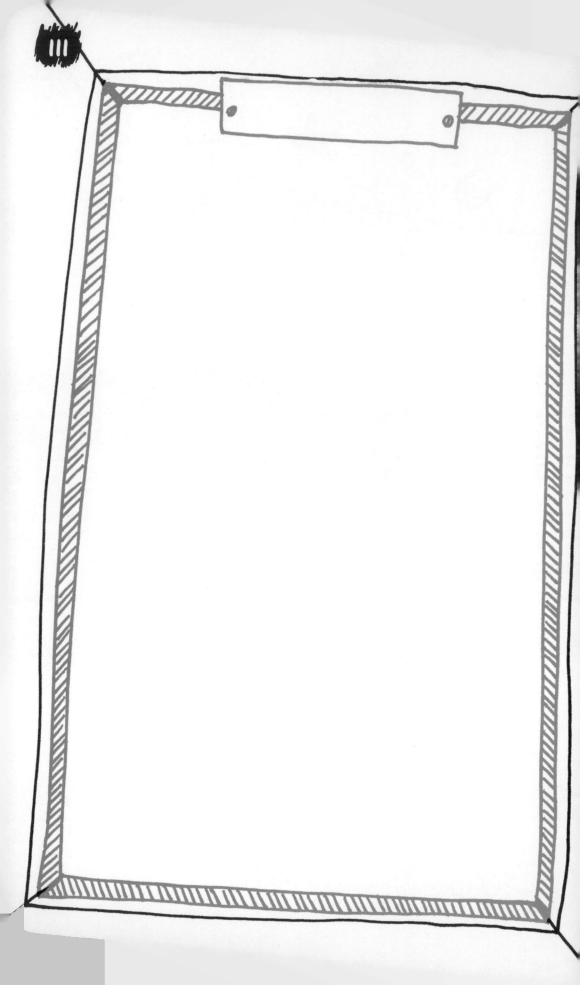

What did you dream about last night?

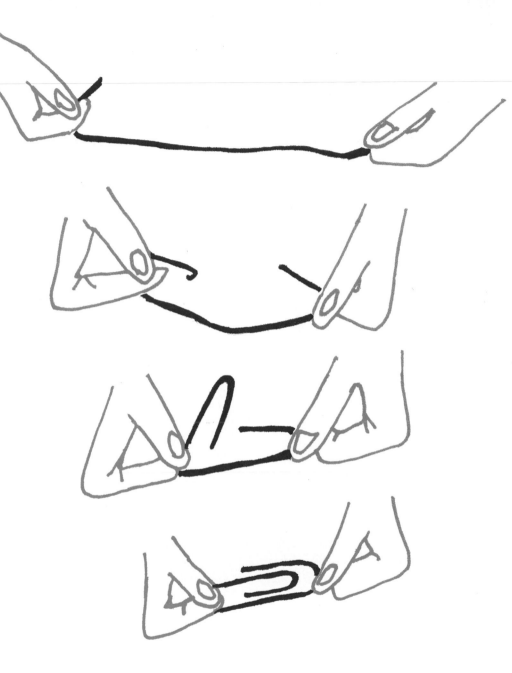

DRAW YOUR HOUSE BY STICKING DOWN PAPERCLIPS
TO MAKE LINES.

SQUEEZE SOME LEMON JUICE INTO A BOWL AND ADD A FEW DROPS OF WATER. DIP A COTTON BUD INTO THE JUICE AND WRITE A SECRET MESSAGE ON THIS PAGE. LEAVE TO DRY AND IT'LL BECOME INVISIBLE. WHEN YOU'RE READY TO REVEAL THE MESSAGE JUST HOLD THE PAGE UP TO A LIGHT BULB.

PLAY NOUGHTS AND CROSSES WITH A FRIEND.

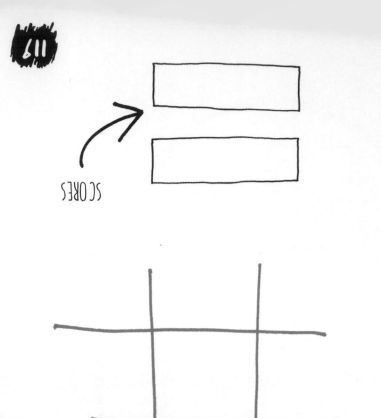

SCORES

PICK ONE OF THESE DESIGNS AND DRAW IT ON

TO YOUR FACE WITH FACE PAINTS OR MAKE-UP.

Complete this dot-to-dot backwards. To begin you'll have to find the highest number.

37

38

39

21

20

19

18

40

41

42

44

43

45

46

47

48

49

50

51

52

53

54

55

56

57

58

59

60

61

62

63

64

65

111

118

COLOUR IN THEN CUT OUT PAGE 125
AND FOLD IT INTO A BOX. TELL FRIENDS
YOU'VE PUT SOMETHING DANGEROUS INSIDE
AND SEE IF THEY DARE TO OPEN IT.

1. CUT THE SOLID LINES.
2. FOLD THE DOTTED LINES.
3. GLUE THE SHADED AREAS.

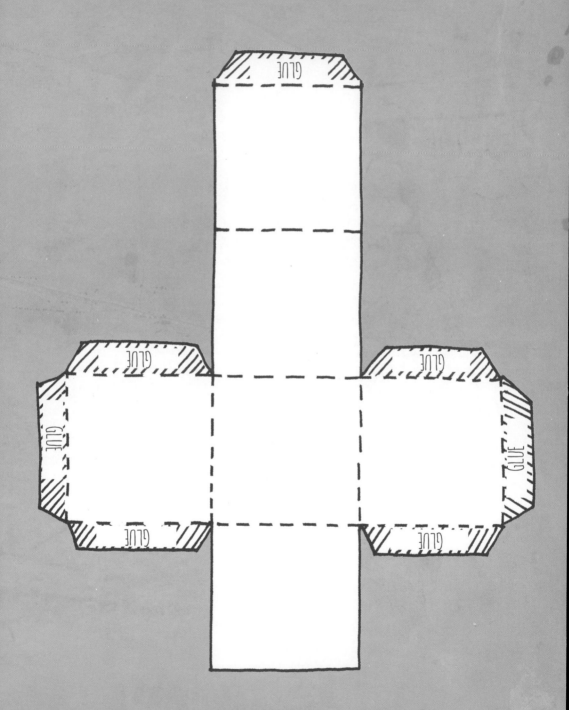

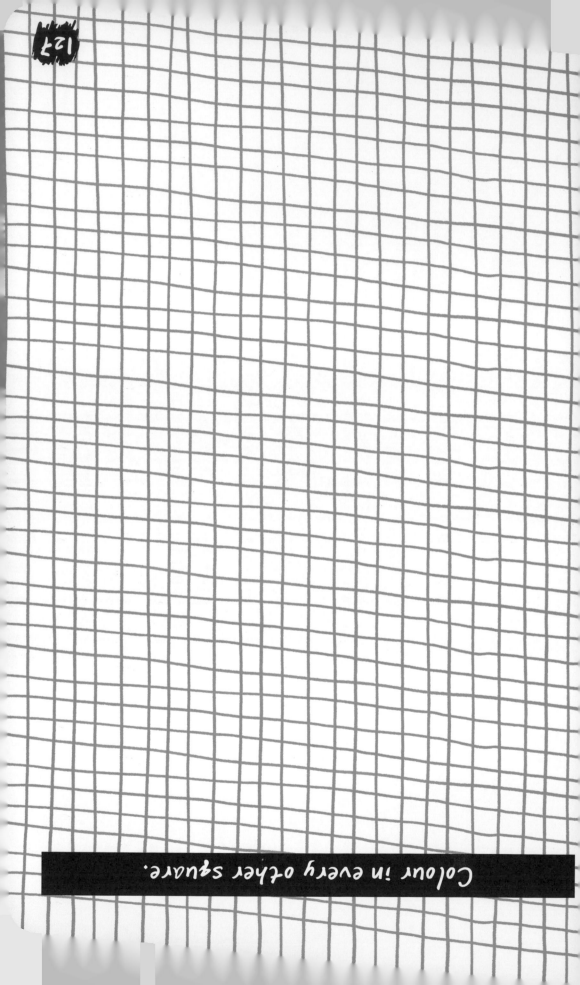

127

Colour in every other square.

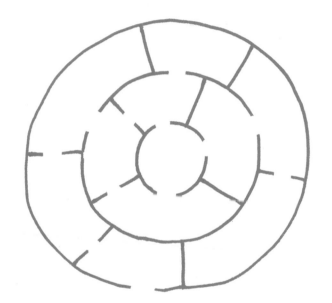

CREATE A MAZE THAT DOESN'T HAVE AN

ENTRY OR AN EXIT. FILL BOTH PAGES.

STARE REALLY HARD AT THESE PAGES

FOR 5 MINUTES. DOES ANYTHING HAPPEN?

WRITE THE ANSWER TO 74 + 22 + 11
IN MORSE CODE.

WRITE YOUR BIRTH DATE IN MORSE CODE.

WRITE THE DATE YOU BOUGHT OR RECEIVED
THIS BOOK IN MORSE CODE.

STICK A COBWEB ON THESE PAGES.

MAKE YOUR OWN FLICK BOOK WITH A SCENE THAT WORKS FORWARDS AND BACKWARDS.

Instructions:

1) Cut out the squares on page 137.

2) Stack them together and secure with a bulldog clip.

3) Draw in your sequence, working from the top page to the bottom page.

4) Flick from top to bottom and then bottom to top to see your scene play forwards and backwards.

Cut out this page and swap it with your favourite page in the book. Stick the pages back in with tape.

SPRAY THIS PAGE WITH PERFUME SO IT SMELLS NICE.

CONGRATULAT... ON OPENING THIS KOOB!

EXPECTING PAGE 1?

NOT A CHANCE! IF YOU HAVEN'T ALREADY FIGURED IT OUT
FROM THE TITLE, KOOB IS A BACKWARDS BOOK, SO TURN
TO THE BACK AND FLIP IT UPSIDE DOWN TO USE IT.
THEN DOODLE, CUT, STICK, FOLD AND SCRIBBLE
YOUR WAY TO THE FRONT!

144